D1490331

The BENDON name, logo and
Tear and Share are trademarks of
Bendon, Ashland, OH 44805.

Copyright © 2015 Disney Enterprises, Inc.
All rights reserved.

Tinker Bell and Terence fly to the fairy camp together.

© Disney

Everyone is busy helping to bring the season of summer to the mainland.

© Disney

After a rough flight, Cheese and Blaze arrive at the fairy camp.

© Disney

Clank and Bobble bring too much stuff!
Use the special tool code to find out the Tinker's Motto.

D R A E B P

___ ___ ___ ___ ___ ___ ___ ___ ___ ___ ___ ___ ___!

Answer: Be prepared!

© Disney

To find out what Tinker Bell tells her friends, replace each
letter below with the one that comes before it in the alphabet.

J I B W F   G B J U I

J O   Q F P Q M F .

© Disney

Answer: I have faith in people.

An amazing machine arrives
and Tinker Bell can't wait to see it!

© Disney

Help Tinker Bell find her way to the car.

START

FINISH

© Disney

Dr. Griffiths and his daughter, Lizzy,
are spending the summer in the country.

© Disney

Tinker Bell wants to talk about the car, but Vidia doesn't want listen.

Look for 5 things that are missing in the bottom picture.

© Disney

Lizzy finds a very unusual butterfly and shows it to her father.

© Disney

Circle the butterfly that matches the one with Dr. Griffiths.

Lizzy made something special!

To find out what it is, go around the circle twice starting with the letter A, and write every other letter on the lines below.

→A

Y   H

E   F

R   O

S   A

I   U

___ ___ ___ ___ ___

___ ___ ___ ___

Answer: A Fairy House.

© Disney

Vidia's wings are wet, so she can't fly.

© Disney

Tinker Bell wants to take the buttons back to the fairy camp.

How many buttons can you count?

© Disney

Vidia thinks the fairy house is a trap,
but Tinker Bell doesn't believe her.

© Disney

Lizzy is taking Tinker Bell
and the fairy house to show her father.

© Disney

Lizzy has a cat named Mr. Twitches and he wants to chase Tinker Bell!

Look for 5 things that are missing in the bottom picture.

© Disney

Answer: Lizzy's bow, patch of fur on Mr. Twitches's right shoulder, Vidia's left hand, the ring on the top of the cage, the bars at the bottom of the cage.

Help Vidia choose the right path back to the fairy camp.

3

2

1

Answer: 3

© Disney

Tinker Bell is in trouble and her friends
are going to rescue her!

© Disney

Everyone is helping Clank and Bobble build the boat.

© Disney

Find out what Lizzy tells Tinker Bell.

Begin at the P and write the letters in order on the blanks as they appear from left to right.

```
P   L   E
A   S   E
D   O   N
T   B   E
A   F   R
A   I   D
```

_ _ _ _ _ _   _ _ _ _   ,

_ _ _ _ _ _ _

© Disney

Answer: Please don't be afraid

Lizzy likes to draw pictures of fairies.
How many fairy drawings can you count?

© Disney

Dr. Griffiths tells Lizzy that fairies are not real!

© Disney

Dr. Griffiths wants Lizzy to study science
and he gives her a field journal.

© Disney

The rescue boat is almost ready to go!

© Disney

FAITH TRUST PIXIE DUST.

How many times can you find each word in the puzzle?

```
D T H T S U R T
U E T T R U S T
F I I T S U D A
A X A X R E D F
I I F T I U U A
T P S X S P S I
H U I T S U R T
D P I X I E D H
```

© Disney

It's time to launch the boat and rescue Tinker Bell.

© Disney

Help the rescue boat through the water maze.

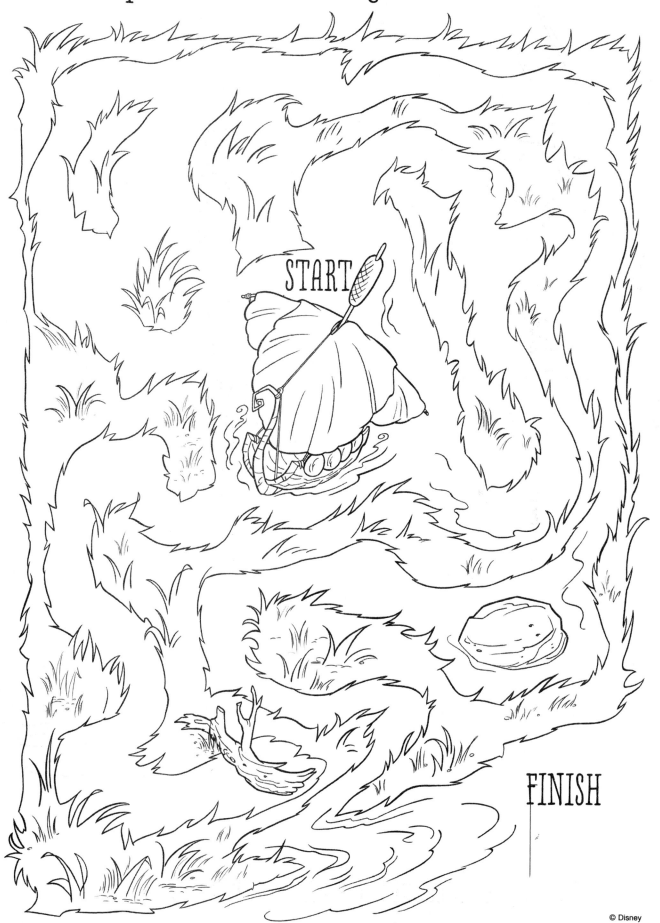

START

FINISH

© Disney

The rescue boat is heading straight for a waterfall!

Look for 5 things that are missing in the bottom picture.

© Disney

Answer: Grass on the shore, ropes at the top of the sail, Fawn, mushroom cap on the side of the boat, moss on the stones.

Silvermist saves her friends
by making a bridge with the water.

© Disney

Vidia knows that the buttons will lead them to Tinker Bell.
Which button trail leads to Lizzy's house?

START

FINISH

© Disney

It's time for Tinker Bell to go back to the fairy world.

© Disney

Lizzy wants to show her father the Fairy Field Journal and Tinker Bell has a plan to help her.

© Disney

Vidia and the fairies are trying to find the
road that will take them to Tinker Bell.

© Disney

Vidia is stuck in the mud,
but Iridessa bends the light and saves her friends!

© Disney

Connect the dots to see what pulls Vidia out of the mud.

After an exciting day,
Lizzy shows Tinker Bell how to have a tea party.

© Disney

Tinker Bell wants to fix the leaks,
so Lizzy can spend time with her father.

© Disney

Find and circle these six things Tinker Bell needs to fix the leaks.

© Disney

Tinker Bell can fix anything, even a leaky roof.

© Disney

Tinker Bell looks at the butterfly Dr. Griffiths has captured.

Look for 5 things that are different in the bottom picture.

© Disney

Answer: Tink's hair, a leaf from Tink's skirt, butterfly's antenna, ribbon bookmark, pen

Where's Tinker Bell?
Find and circle her in the picture.

© Disney

Find out what Dr. Griffiths says to Lizzy.

Replace each letter below with the one that comes after it in the alphabet.

‾‾ ‾‾ ‾‾
S G D

‾‾ ‾‾ ‾‾ ‾‾ ‾‾ ‾‾ ‾‾ ‾‾ ‾‾
A T S S D Q E K X

‾‾ ‾‾ ‾‾ ‾‾ ‾‾ ‾‾ !
H R   F N M D

© Disney

Answer: The butterfly is gone!

Vidia thinks it's her fault that Tinker Bell is in trouble,
but the other fairies don't believe it.

© Disney

The fairies are ready to rescue Tinker Bell.

© Disney

Use the special code to find out what Lizzy tells Tinker Bell.

A F H I W R Y S

" _ "

Answer: I wish I was a fairy.

© Disney

Tinker Bell is going to teach Lizzy how to fly like a fairy!

How many pixie dust sparkles can you count?

© Disney

Answer: 35

Flying is not as easy as it looks, but it sure is fun!

© Disney

The rescue team has arrived at Lizzy's house
and they work together to get inside.

© Disney

Mr. Twitches is trying to catch the fairies,
so they make a bridge out of dishes.

© Disney

Dr. Griffiths does not believe that Lizzy has a real fairy.

© Disney

Find out what Lizzy says to her father.

Follow the line from each letter to an empty box, then write the letter in that box.

R E R A S L A E E I R A I F

" ☐ ☐ ☐ ☐ ☐ ☐ ☐ ☐ ☐ ☐ ☐ ☐ ☐ ☐ !"

Answer: Fairies are real!

© Disney

Vidia saves Tinker Bell, but gets trapped in the jar!

Hold this page up to a mirror to find out where Dr. Griffiths is taking Vidia.

THE MUSEUM.

© Disney

Answer: The museum.

Lizzy wants to help the fairies save Vidia.
Look for 5 things that are missing in the bottom picture.

Answer: Wood beam on ceiling, Lizzy's braid, the leaf on Tink's braid, Fawn's dress, Clank's wingtip.

© Disney

With faith, trust and pixie dust, Lizzy can fly!

© Disney

Connect the dots to see London.

© Disney

Can you match the missing pieces in the picture?

Write the letter in the place where each one belongs.

A
B
C

© Disney

Answer: 1-B, 2-A, 3-C

Nothing can stop Tinker Bell!

© Disney

Dr. Griffiths doesn't have to understand, he just needs to believe.

To find out what Dr. Griffiths tells Lizzy, begin at the "I" and write the letters in order on the blanks as they appear from left to right.

I	S	H	A
L	L	N	E
V	E	R	D
O	U	B	T
Y	O	U	A
G	A	I	N

— —— —— —— —— ——

——— —— —— —— —— —— ———

—— —— —— —— —— ———.

© Disney

Answer: I shall never doubt you again.

It's time to go home.

Find the right path back to the Griffiths' house.

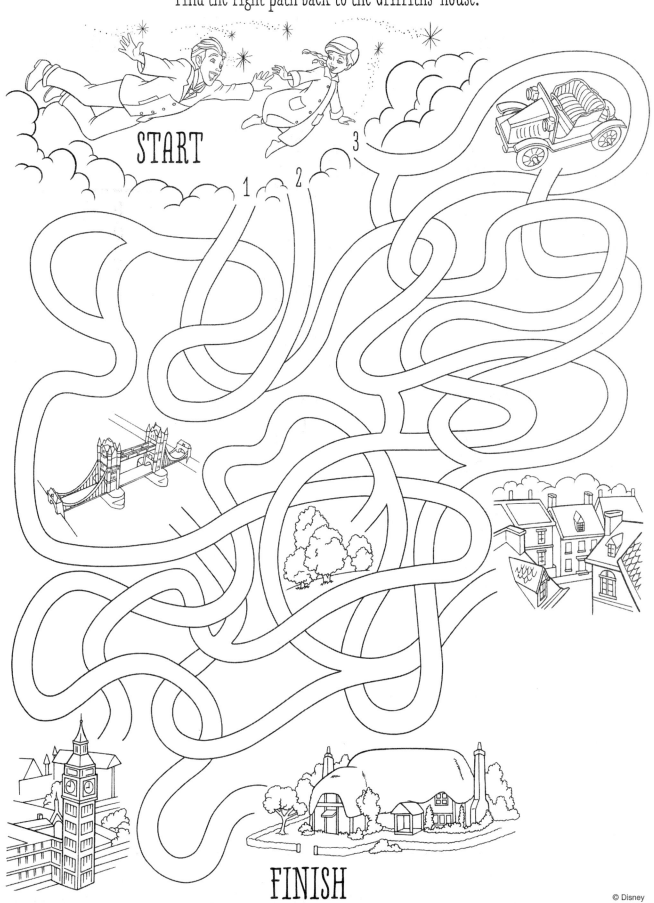

START

1 2 3

FINISH

© Disney

It's a beautiful day for a fairy tea party!

© Disney

It's the most wonderful tea party in the world!

© Disney

Anything is possible with a little faith, trust and pixie dust!

© Disney